Core Knowledge Language Arts®

Unit 3
Workbook

Skills Strand
KINDERGARTEN

Amplify learning.

Core Knowledge®

ISBN 978-1-61700-175-8

Printed in the USA
08 LSCOW 2020

Unit 3
Workbook

This Workbook contains worksheets that accompany many of the lessons from the *Teacher Guide* for Unit 3. Each worksheet is identified by the lesson number in which it is used. The worksheets in this book do not include written instructions for students because the instructions would have words that are not decodable. Teachers will explain these worksheets to the students orally, using the instructions in the Teacher Guide. The Workbook is a student component, which means each student should have a Workbook.

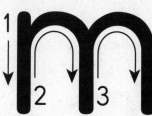

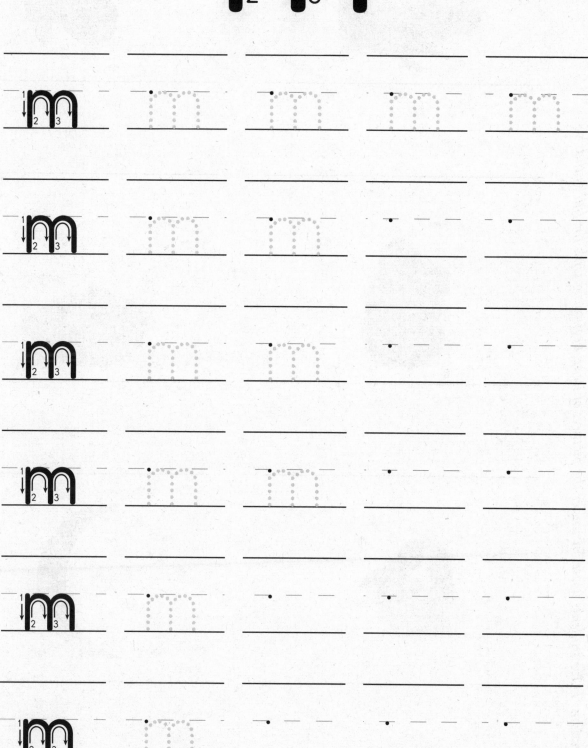

Directions: Have students trace and copy the letter. The motion can be described as 1. short line down, 2. bump; 3.) bump. Student should say the sound as he or she writes the letter.

2 *Unit 3*

Directions: Have students trace and copy the letter. The motion can be described as 1. circle to the left, 2. short line down.
Student should say the sound as he or she writes the letter.

4   *Unit 3*

Name _____

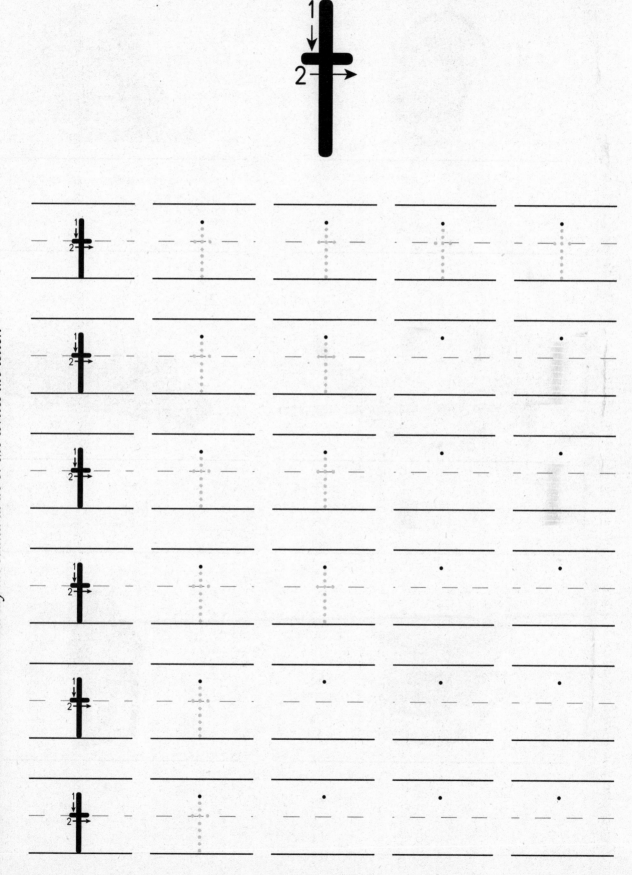

Directions: Have students trace and copy the letter. The motion can be described as 1. long line down (lift), 2. short line across. Student should say the sound as he or she writes the letter.

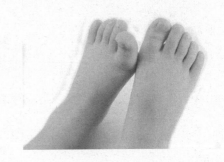

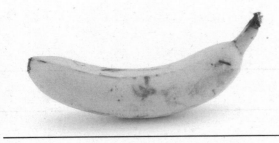

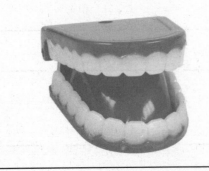

Directions: Have students write 't' under the pictures of items beginning with the /t/ sound.

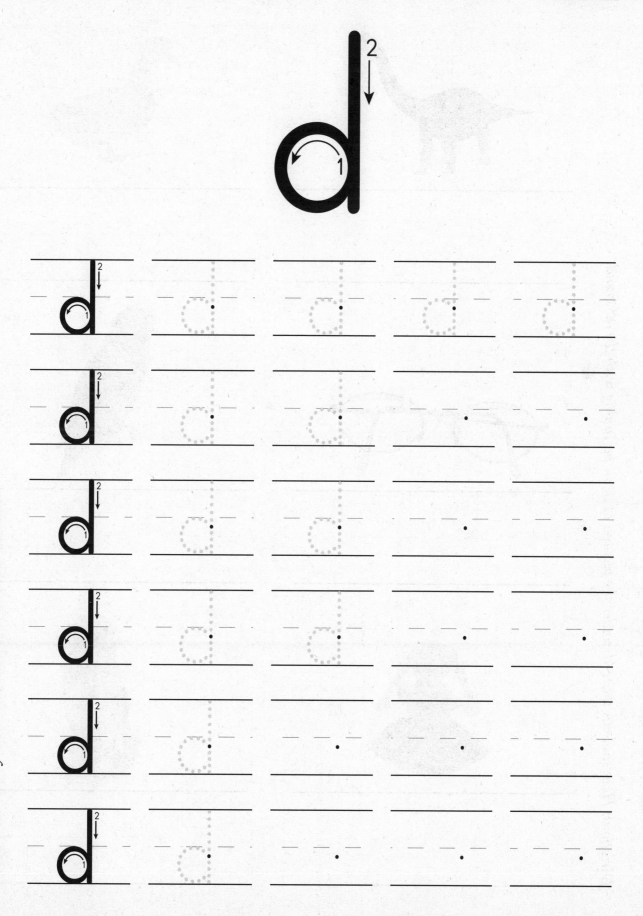

Directions: Have students trace and copy the letter. The motion can be described as 1. circle to the left, 2. long line down. Student should say the sound as he or she writes the letter.

Dear Family Member,

Please help your child cut out the picture cards on this page. On Worksheet 4.3, have your child glue or tape the cards with pictures beginning with the /m/ sound (moon, monkey, mouse) under the 'm' heading. Next, glue or tape cards with pictures beginning with the /t/ sound (toes, teeth, tiger) under the 't' heading.

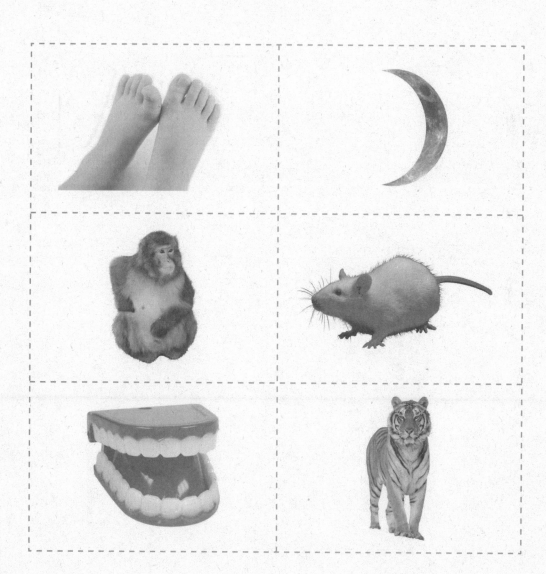

Dear Family Member,

Please have your child glue the pictures from Worksheet 4.2 here. Affix pictures of things beginning with the /m/ sound under the 'm' heading and pictures beginning with the /t/ sound under the 't' heading.

1. mad

2. dad

3. mat

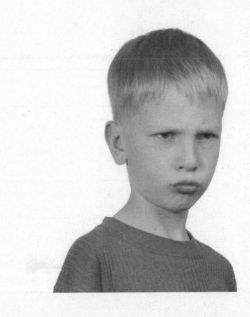

Name _____

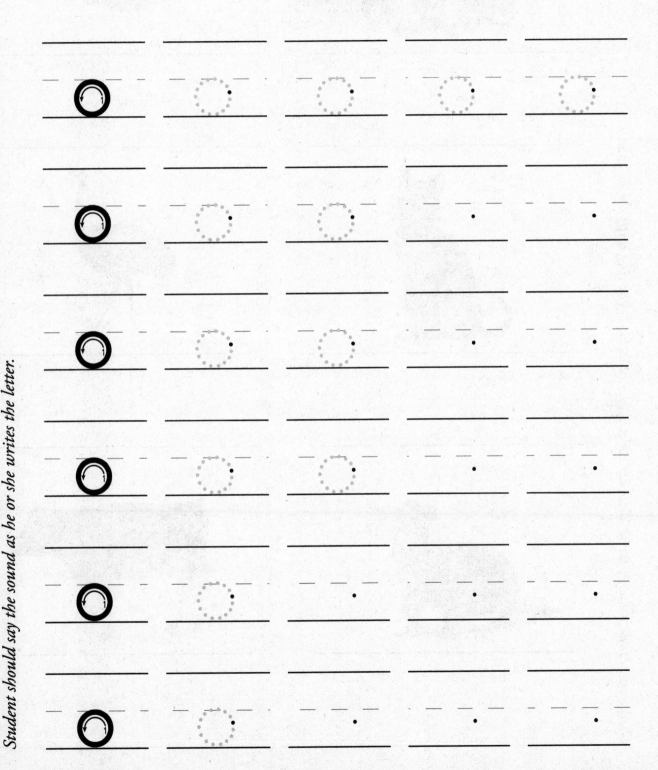

Dear Family Member,

In class we have been learning some letter-sound correspondences. Your child is learning to read words printed in lowercase letters by saying the sounds and blending them to make a word. Some words your child should be able to blend and read with practice are printed below. Help your child cut out the word cards. Show the cards to your child and have him or her blend and read them. Please encourage your child to read the words by saying the individual sounds and blending them together to make the word. Do not try to teach your child to recognize a word as a whole unit. It can be difficult to make sounds and blend them. If that is the case for your child, provide help by saying the individual sounds and asking your child to say the whole word, i.e., blend the sounds into a word.

As an extension of this activity, you may ask your child to copy the words on a sheet of paper and/or copy selected words and illustrate them.

Please keep the word cards for future practice.

ad	dot	dad
am	mad	mom
at	mat	tot

Directions: Have students trace and copy the letter 'c'. The motion can be described as 1. most of a circle to the left. Student should say the sound as he or she writes the letter.

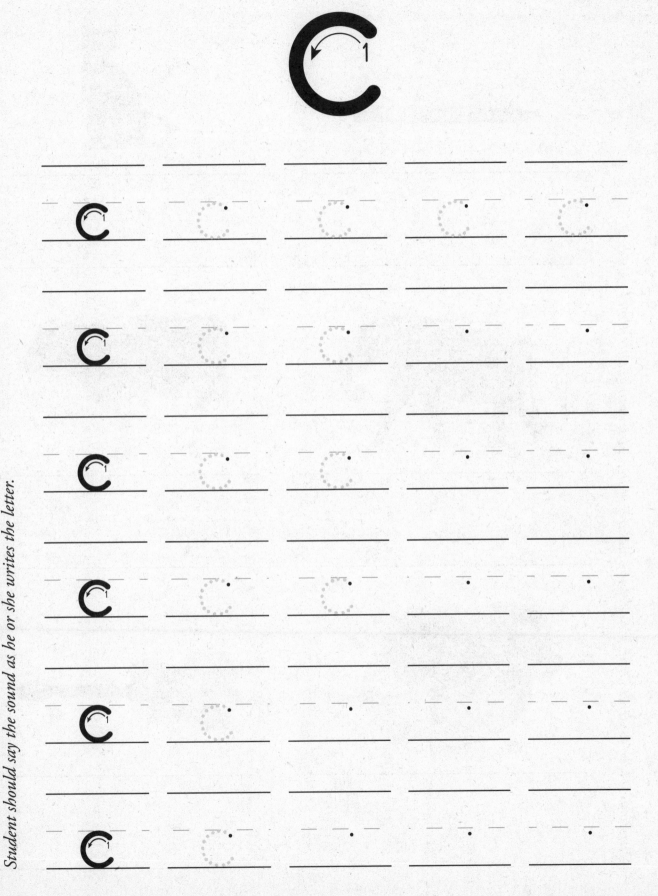

20   *Unit 3*

Dear Family Member,

Please help your child cut out the picture cards on this page. On Worksheet 7.3, have your child glue or tape the cards with pictures beginning with the /a/ sound (ax, apple, alligator) under the 'a' heading. Next, glue or tape cards with pictures beginning with the /o/ sound (octopus, otter, ostrich) under the 'o' heading.

Dear Family Member,

Please have your child glue or tape the pictures from Worksheet 7.2 here. Affix pictures beginning with the /a/ sound under the 'a' heading and pictures beginning with the /o/ sound under the 'o' heading.

a | o

Name _____

Directions: Have students trace and copy the letter 'g'. The motion can be described as 1. circle to the left, 2. fish hook ending below the bottom line. Student should say the sound as he or she writes the letter.

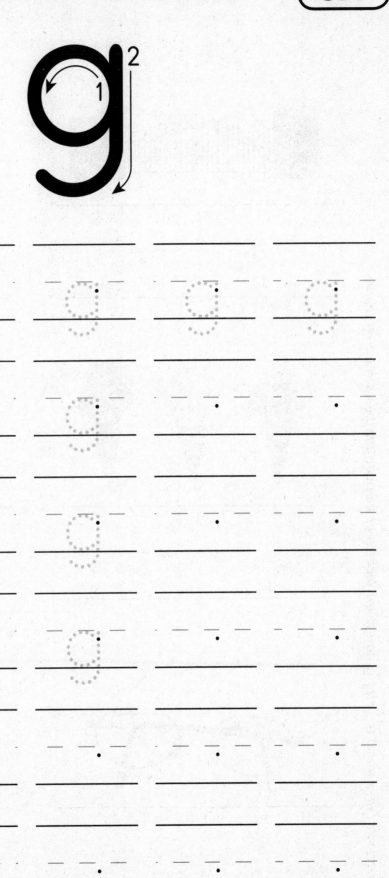

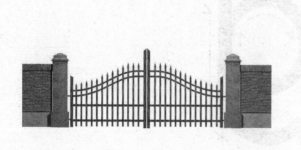

Directions: Have students write 'g' under the pictures of items beginning with the /g/ sound.

Directions: Have students trace and copy the letters and words. The motion for "i" can be described as 1. short line down (lift), 2. dot on top. Student should say the sound as he or she writes the letter.

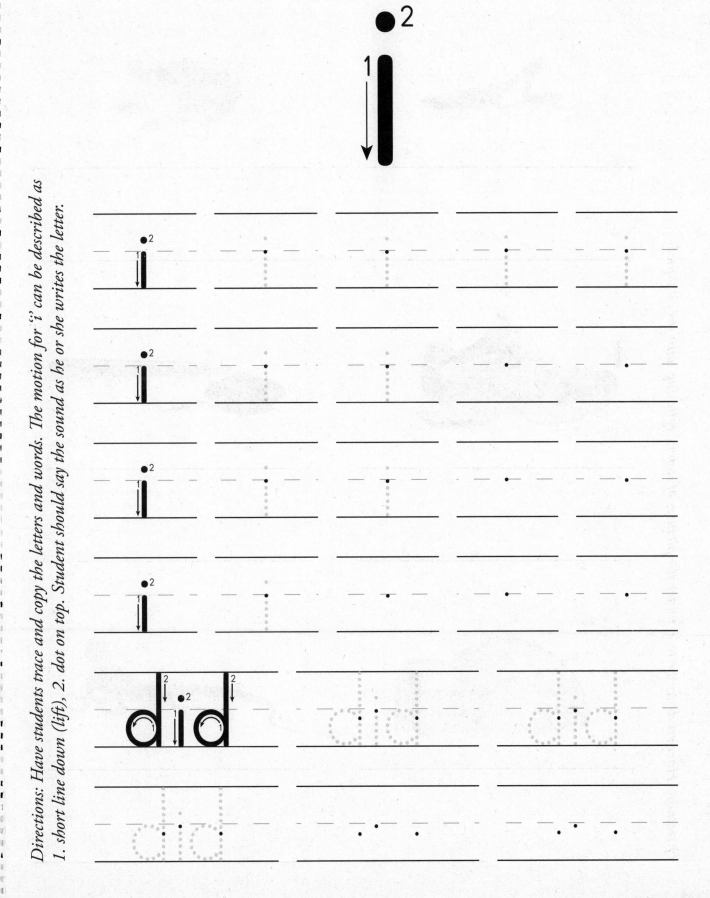

Directions: Have students write 'i' under the pictures of items beginning with the /i/ sound.

Name _____

Dear Family Member,

Help your child cut out the letter cards. Arrange the cards to make the words "mat," "dad," "got," "cat," "dog," "dig," "did," "mad," "tag," and "cot." Have your child blend and read the words.

Handwriting Practice: Have your child copy the words on a sheet of paper.

m	a	t
<u>d</u>	o	c
g	i	<u>d</u>

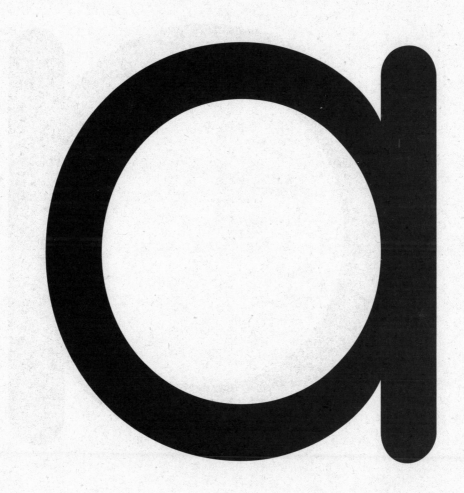

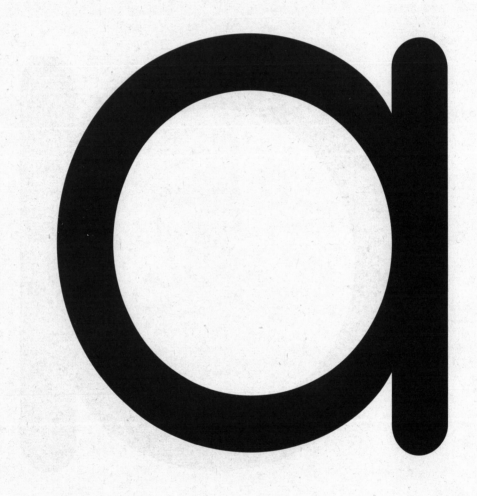

Directions: Have students hold up this worksheet when you say lil.

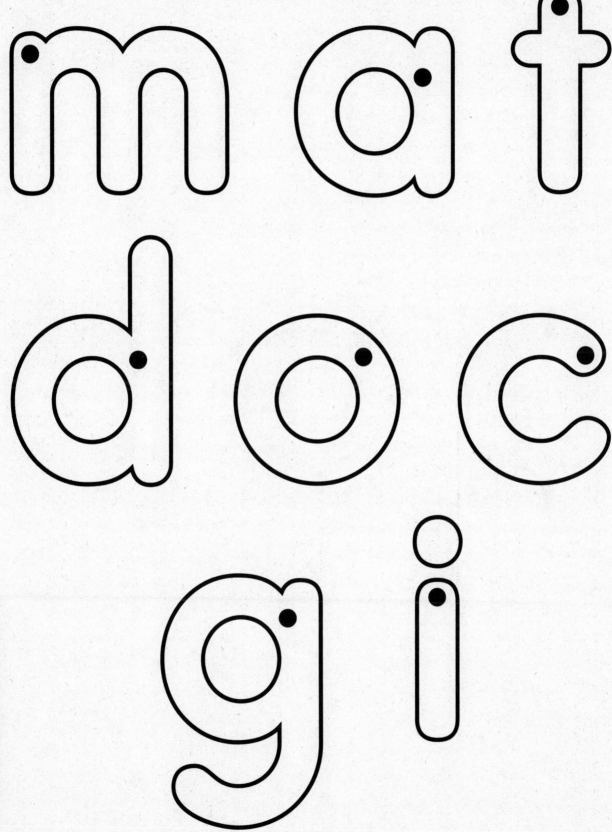

Directions: Have students trace each letter several times, using a different-colored crayon each time. Make sure students start to trace the letter at the black dot.

16.3

t a m

c o b

i g

Dear Family Member,

Have your child draw a line from each word on the left to the matching picture. If necessary, identify the pictures for your child. Please complete the back of the worksheet in the same manner.

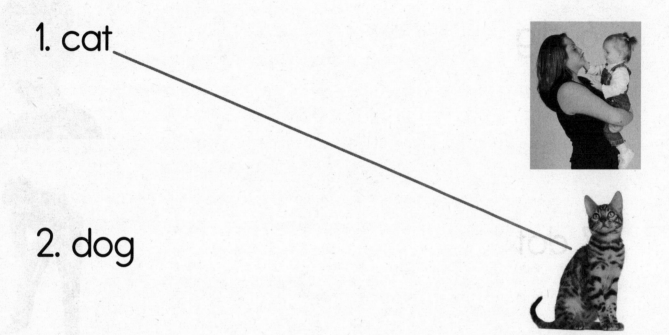

1. cat

2. dog

3. tag

4. mom

5. mad

6. dig

7. dot

8. dad

9. mat

1. cat

_____

\- \- \- \- \- \- \- \-

_____

2. dog

_____

\- \- \- \- \- \- \- \-

_____

3. dam

_____

\- \- \- \- \- \- \- \-

_____

Directions: Have students copy each word under its matching picture.

4. dig

_____

- - - - - - - - - - - - -

_____

5. dad

_____

- - - - - - - - - - - - -

_____

6. cot

_____

- - - - - - - - - - - - -

_____

Record Sheet for Unit 3 Word Reading

Place a check next to each word read correctly. For words that are misread, write exactly what the student says as he sounds out the word. If a student misreads a word, prompt him or her to try to read the word again, letting him or her know their first attempt was incorrect.

WORD	FIRST ATTEMPT	SECOND ATTEMPT/ NOTES
1. cat		
2. mom		
3. dog		
4. tag		
5. mat		
6. dad		
7. dot		
8. mad		
9. dig		
10. cot		
TOTAL CORRECT	/30	

SUBTOTAL:

'c' > /k/ (1,10) ____/2   'a' > /a/ (1,4,5,6,8) ____/5   't' > /t/ (1,4,5,7,10) ____/5

'm' > /m/ (2,5,8) ____/4   'o' > /o/ (2,3,7,10) ____/4   'd' > /d/ (3,6,7,8,9) ____/6

'g' > /g/ (3,4,9) ____/3   'i' > /i/ (9) ____/1

1.   cot   cat   mat   dot

2.   dog   got   did   tag

3.   at   cat   mad   mat

4.   dot   tot   got   dog

5.   gig   cot   dig   dim

Directions: In each row, have students circle the word the teacher pronounces.

6. mad   mom   dot   dim

7. tot   dig   tag   dad

8. cat   did   dad   dog

9. mad   tad   mat   dad

10. cat   mat   got   cot

Dear Family Member,

Help your child cut out the word cards. Show the cards to your child and have your child blend and read them. Please encourage your child to read the words by saying the individual sounds and then blending them together to read the word. Do not try to teach your child to read whole words. It can be difficult to make sounds and blend them. If that is the case for your child, help by saying each individual sound and ask your child to say the whole word, i.e., blend the sounds into a word.

Extension: Read the words aloud and have your child write the sounds down, one at a time.

Please keep the cards for future practice.

mom	cat	tag
it	did	dig
got	cot	dim

4. mad

5. cat

6. cot

1. doc

_____ _____
- - - - - - - - - - - - - - - - - -
_____ _____

2. mat

_____ _____
- - - - - - - - - - - - - - - - - -
_____ _____

3. tag

_____ _____
- - - - - - - - - - - - - - - - - -
_____ _____

Name _____

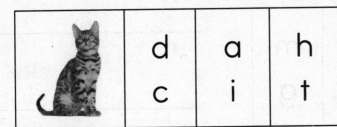

d	a	h
c	i	t

_____

- - - - - - - - - - - - - - - - -

_____

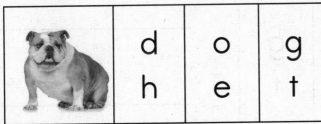

d	o	g
h	e	t

_____

- - - - - - - - - - - - - - - - -

_____

t	o	g
c	a	t

_____

- - - - - - - - - - - - - - - - -

_____

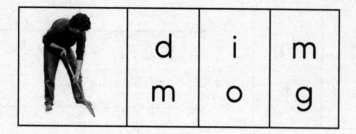

d	i	m
m	o	g

_____
- - - - - - - - - - -
_____

t	o	g
c	a	t

_____
- - - - - - - - - - -
_____

c	a	d
m	o	c

_____
- - - - - - - - - - -
_____

Dear Family Member,

Please help your child cut out the picture cards on this page. On Worksheet 13.3, have your child glue or tape the cards with pictures beginning with the /i/ sound (insect, igloo, ink) under the 'i' heading. Next, glue or tape the cards with pictures beginning with the /o/ sound (octopus, otter, ostrich) under the 'o' heading.

Dear Family Member,

Please have your child glue or tape the pictures from Worksheet 13.2 here. Affix pictures beginning with the /i/ sound under the 'i' heading and pictures beginning with the /o/ sound under the 'o' heading.

i o

Directions: Have students write each word under its matching picture.

1. dad

_____

- - - - - - - - - - - - - -

_____

2. dog

_____

- - - - - - - - - - - - - -

_____

3. cod

_____

- - - - - - - - - - - - - -

_____

4. dot

_____

- - - - - - - - - - - - - - - - -

_____

5. mad

_____

- - - - - - - - - - - - - - - - -

_____

6. dam

_____

- - - - - - - - - - - - - - - - -

_____

| | t / c | o / a | g / t |

| | d / m | o / a | g / t |

| | t / c | o / a | g / t |

Directions: For each picture, have students circle the letters that spell the name of the depicted item.
Students should then write the name of the item on the line.

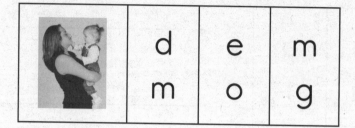

	d m	e o	m g

_____
- - - - - - - - - - - - - - - -
_____

	c m	a o	g t

_____
- - - - - - - - - - - - - - - -
_____

	d m	a o	d g

_____
- - - - - - - - - - - - - - - -
_____

Dear Family Member,

Help your child cut out the two circles. Pin the smaller circle on top of the larger circle with a brass fastener. Ask your child to spin the smaller circle to make words. Have your child blend and read the words he or she makes.

Handwriting Practice: Ask your child to copy the words on a sheet of paper.

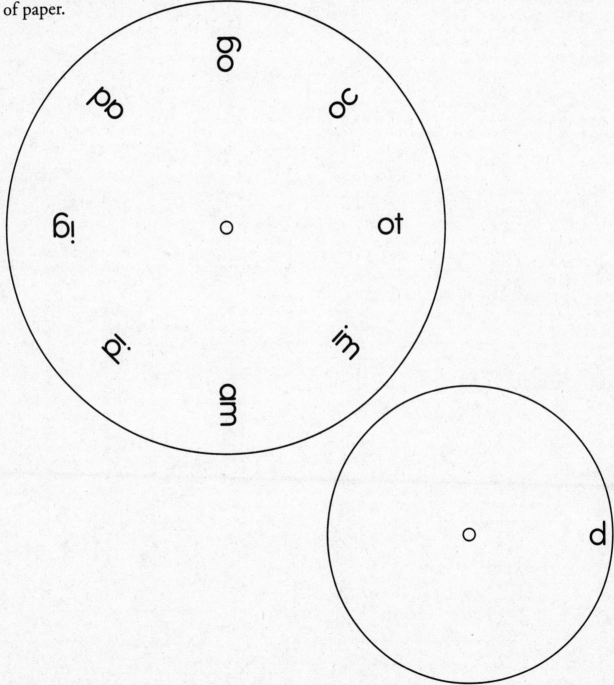

~~dog~~   tag

dad   cot

dog

Directions: Have students write each word under its matching picture.

cat	doc
dig	mad

_____

- - - - - - - - - - -

_____

_____

- - - - - - - - - - -

_____

_____

- - - - - - - - - - -

_____

_____

- - - - - - - - - - -

_____

1. cot

_____

- - - - - - - - - - - - -

_____

2. mom

_____

- - - - - - - - - - - - -

_____

3. cat

_____

- - - - - - - - - - - - -

_____

4. dot

5. dad

6. dam

c

c

a

a

g

g

d

d

Directions: Have students trace and copy the letters. Encourage students to say the sounds while writing the letters.

Directions: Have students trace and copy the letters. Encourage students to say the sounds while writing the letters.

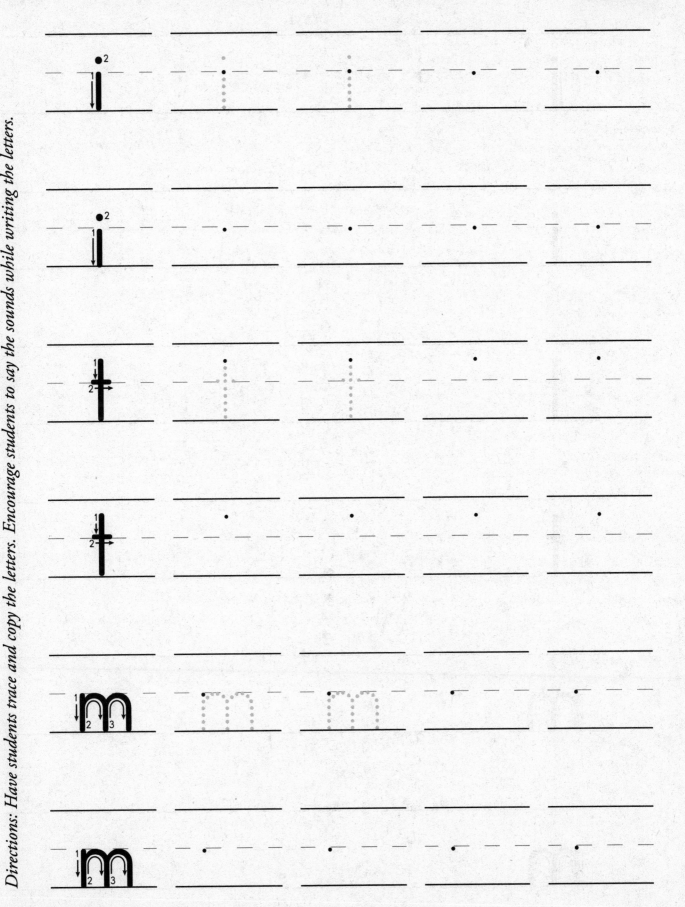

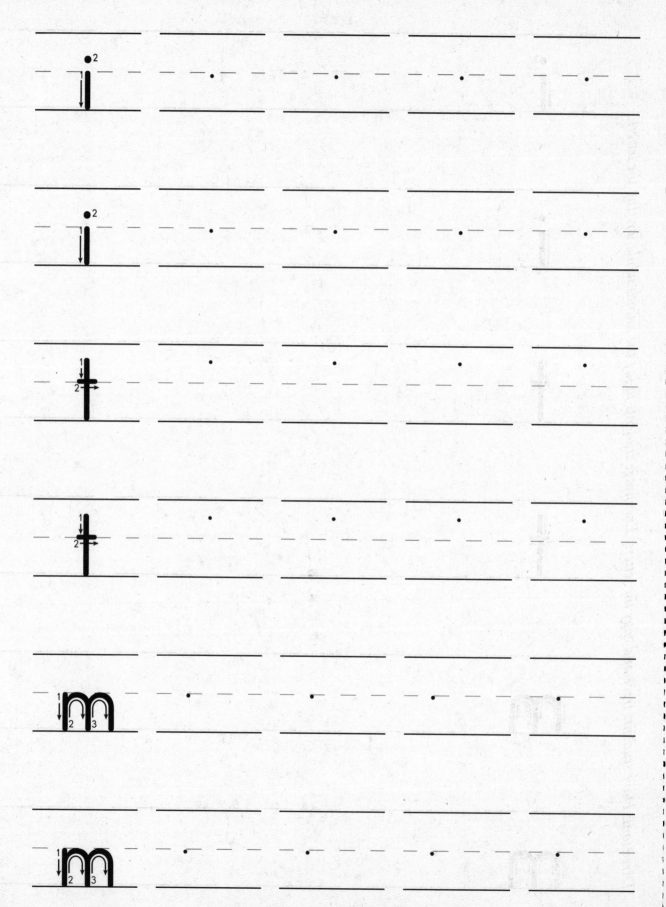

Directions: Have students trace and copy the words. Encourage students to say the sounds while writing the letters.

at

cat

dot

dog

dig

cot

at

cat

dot

dog

dig

cot

Directions: Have students trace and copy the words. Encourage students to say the sounds while writing the letters.

it

did

dad

dim

tag

mad

Directions: Have students trace and copy the words. Encourage students to say the sounds while writing the letters.

it

did

dad

dim

tag

mad

dad   at   tic

~~mom~~   got   cot

Directions: Have students sort the six words by their first sounds, copying each word twice.

m

a

d

g

t

c

mom   mom

dot	cod	~~tag~~
got	it	mom

Directions: Have students sort the six words by their first sounds, copying each word twice.

t

g

m

d

c

i

tag   tag

© 2013 Core Knowledge Foundation

cat   cod   dad

did   ~~dig~~   dog

Directions: Have students sort the six words by their middle sounds, copying each word twice.

i

i

a

a

o

o

dig   dig

	d c	a i	h d

●	d h	o e	g t

	d c	o a	m t

Directions: For each picture, have students circle the letters that spell the name of the depicted item. Students should then write the name of the item on the line.

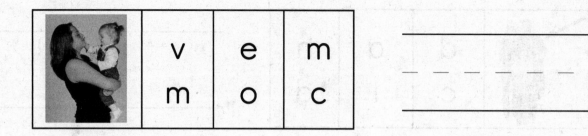

| | v | e | m |
| | m | o | c |

_____

| | d | a | g |
| | m | o | c |

_____

| | c | a | d |
| | m | o | c |

_____

CORE KNOWLEDGE LANGUAGE ARTS

SERIES EDITOR-IN-CHIEF
E. D. Hirsch, Jr.

PRESIDENT
Linda Bevilacqua

EDITORIAL STAFF
Carolyn Gosse, Senior Editor - Preschool
Khara Turnbull, Materials Development Manager
Michelle L. Warner, Senior Editor - Listening & Learning

Mick Anderson
Robin Blackshire
Maggie Buchanan
Paula Coyner
Sue Fulton
Sara Hunt
Erin Kist
Robin Luecke
Rosie McCormick
Cynthia Peng
Liz Pettit
Ellen Sadler
Deborah Samley
Diane Auger Smith
Sarah Zelinke

DESIGN AND GRAPHICS STAFF
Scott Ritchie, Creative Director

Kim Berrall
Michael Donegan
Liza Greene
Matt Leech
Bridget Moriarty
Lauren Pack

CONSULTING PROJECT MANAGEMENT SERVICES
ScribeConcepts.com

ADDITIONAL CONSULTING SERVICES
Ang Blanchette
Dorrit Green
Carolyn Pinkerton

ACKNOWLEDGMENTS

These materials are the result of the work, advice, and encouragement of numerous individuals over many years. Some of those singled out here already know the depth of our gratitude; others may be surprised to find themselves thanked publicly for help they gave quietly and generously for the sake of the enterprise alone. To helpers named and unnamed we are deeply grateful.

CONTRIBUTORS TO EARLIER VERSIONS OF THESE MATERIALS
Susan B. Albaugh, Kazuko Ashizawa, Nancy Braier, Kathryn M. Cummings, Michelle De Groot, Diana Espinal, Mary E. Forbes, Michael L. Ford, Ted Hirsch, Danielle Knecht, James K. Lee, Diane Henry Leipzig, Martha G. Mack, Liana Mahoney, Isabel McLean, Steve Morrison, Juliane K. Munson, Elizabeth B. Rasmussen, Laura Tortorelli, Rachael L. Shaw, Sivan B. Sherman, Miriam E. Vidaver, Catherine S. Whittington, Jeannette A. Williams

We would like to extend special recognition to Program Directors Matthew Davis and Souzanne Wright who were instrumental to the early development of this program.

SCHOOLS
We are truly grateful to the teachers, students, and administrators of the following schools for their willingness to field test these materials and for their invaluable advice: Capitol View Elementary, Challenge Foundation Academy (IN), Community Academy Public Charter School, Lake Lure Classical Academy, Lepanto Elementary School, New Holland Core Knowledge Academy, Paramount School of Excellence, Pioneer Challenge Foundation Academy, New York City PS 26R (The Carteret School), PS 30X (Wilton School), PS 50X (Clara Barton School), PS 96Q, PS 102X (Joseph O. Loretan), PS 104Q (The Bays Water), PS 214K (Michael Friedsam), PS 223Q (Lyndon B. Johnson School), PS 308K (Clara Cardwell), PS 333Q (Goldie Maple Academy), Sequoyah Elementary School, South Shore Charter Public School, Spartanburg Charter School, Steed Elementary School, Thomas Jefferson Classical Academy, Three Oaks Elementary, West Manor Elementary.

And a special thanks to the CKLA Pilot Coordinators Anita Henderson, Yasmin Lugo-Hernandez, and Susan Smith, whose suggestions and day-to-day support to teachers using these materials in their classrooms was critical.